The Story of
Iron Ore Mining
in West Cumbria

The Story of Iron Ore Mining in West Cumbria

Mervyn Dodd

With a contribution by Maureen Fisher

Foreword by
David Kelly

Edited by
Susan Beale

Published by
The Cumberland Geological Society

Published by
The Cumberland Geological Society
Quinta
Grizebeck
Kirkby-inFurness
Cumbria LA17 7XJ
www.cumberland-geol-soc.org.uk

Designed by Tom Partridge www.tompartridge.co.uk

Printed and bound by
Printexpress
Unit 1
Sneckyeat Industrial Estate
Hensingham
Whitehaven
Cumbria CA28 8PF
E-mail sales@printex.co.uk

British Library
ISBN 978-0-9558453-1-4

Contents

Foreword by David Kelly   vii

Preface   viii

Acknowledgements   ix

Chapters

1   The Location of the Iron Ore Mines   1
2   The Rise and Fall of Iron Mining   8
3   Lamplugh and Kirkland   18
4   The Frizington area   28
5   Around Cleator Moor   38
6   Egremont and beyond   50
7   Epilogue - The Red Men and their memories   64
     by Maureen Fisher

Index   78

List of Figures   80

Foreword

A visitor travelling through rural West Cumbria between Calder Bridge in the south and Lamplugh in the north will see impressive views of the Lake District Fells to the east and, occasionally, of the Irish Sea and the Solway coasts to the west. On the coast the sight of the Sellafield nuclear plant will doubtless make an impression. The number of small villages and towns with terraced streets of stone cottages may also puzzle the visitor.

However, in the second half of the nineteenth century, and in the first half of the twentieth century a visitor would have seen a world that has now disappeared. Yes, the belt of countryside some 10 miles long hugging the fells would still have had its mountain and coastal views. Prominent features of the landscape, however, would have been pithead winding gear and large heaps of deep-red rock waste. The days would be regulated by the chimes of the steam whistles which announced the start and finish times of the shifts at different mines. Men would have been seen walking home from work with their clothes and skins stained red. The visitor would have been surprised to see rivers like the Ehen running blood-red twice a day when waters from the mines were released into their channels.

This was not just a matter of local interest. Before 1850 the mines in the area were relatively small but then the invention of the Bessemer process of steel manufacture in 1856 made the West Cumbrian hematite ore, with its high purity and low phosphorus content, a highly sought after commodity of national economic importance. Mining settlements like Cleator Moor and Frizington sprang up and towns such as Workington and Barrow in Furness developed iron and steel industries and became Victorian boom towns.

This book reveals this world, telling the stories of the people who lived and worked in the area in times that were tougher than those of today. With guided walks it allows us to explore the landscape and interpret the industrial archaeology. It discusses the origin of the hematite ores, a topic that has long been a matter of debate for geologists. It explains the methods used to mine the ores. I am delighted that Mervyn Dodd, with his encyclopaedic knowledge of the geography and geology of the area, has chosen to tell the story.

David Kelly
President Cumberland Geological Society
December 2009

Preface

This book tells the story of the iron mines and miners of West Cumbria. It illustrates the hardships and dangers the miners faced, their culture and their society, especially in the villages and small towns of Lamplugh and Kirkland, Frizington, Cleator Moor and Egremont, settlements which iron mining either created or at the very least moulded and altered. The good neighbourliness and self-help so characteristic of the local culture are celebrated. The sudden rise and long continued decline of the iron ore mines is described and explained. Why West Cumbria had such rich deposits of iron ore and how such a difficult ore was mined are other themes of the book.

Now is an ideal time for such a book with the last iron mine having ceased production in 2008. Surviving miners are becoming fewer so it is important to record their memories as it is almost 30 years since the last big mine closed. Interest in the mines and men is reviving at a time when it is 15 years since the last comprehensive account was published. So there is a gap this book tries to fill by convincing descriptions of iron mining and its impact on some of the local communities. We illustrate the effect of iron mining on the area and its people then and now.

Acknowledgements

I greatly appreciate the interest, encouragement, advice and help from so many people in West Cumbria. In particular the suggestions made by Betty Marshall of Lamplugh, Harold Borrowdale of High Padstow and the information and advice from Dave Banks of Thornhill about individual chapters have been most helpful. Gilbert Finlinson, the last manager at the Florence Mine, has given great help in identifying the miners on old photographs and explaining the technical details of mining. We have been very pleased to use the wonderful rich seam of material provided by the reminiscences of so many miners now living in and around Frizington

Without the support of the Cumberland Geological Society and its members this book would not have been possible. My editor, Susan Beale, has been a wise and hardworking influence who has improved the organization of the text and made it far more readable. Fred Lawton and David Powell have been a constant help, especially in finding and processing photos and maps which have greatly enhanced the book. I appreciate the careful and accurate proof reading so willingly undertaken by David Livesey.

Financial support from the following sponsors is gratefully acknowledged:

The Curry Fund of the Geologists Association
Arlecdon and Frizington Neighbourhood Forum
Cleator Moor Neighbourhood Forum
Egremont and St. Bees Neighbourhood Forum
Gosforth and Ennerdale Neighbourhood Forum

Chapter 1

The Location of
the Hematite Mines

Hematite is a mineral very rich in iron, 50% or so by weight. It is an iron ore, a material mined for its high iron content. Hematite iron mining began in West Cumberland before 1200 AD and ended in March 2008. For several years around 1880 West Cumberland mines produced over one million tons of hematite annually. Only one other large iron ore mine in the United Kingdom outside present day Cumbria, Llanharry in South Wales, produced similar high-grade ore in any quantity. West and South Cumberland had large reserves, now almost exhausted, of the best iron ore in Great Britain.

The mining area is boomerang shaped and is about 15km by 3km, as shown in Figure 1. The area between Lamplugh (NY 07 20) and Bigrigg (NY 00 13) is the exposed ore field, where the rocks carrying hematite are just below the soil and other unconsolidated material. The concealed ore field is south of Egremont (NY 01 10) where the much younger red St. Bees Sandstones cover and "hide" the ore bearing rocks. This whole area has been affected by earth movements which caused many faults in the rocks, (fractures along which the rocks have moved as shown in the sketch section, Figure 2). Some of these faults carry hematite. The more accessible hematite deposits lie between the old hard rocks of the Lake District to the east and the West Cumberland Coalfield to the west. The map, Figure 1, shows that most of the hematite mines are in the 350 million year old Carboniferous Limestone between Lamplugh and Beckermet. This limestone is a grey rock, occurring in layers or beds, which sometimes form lines of cliffs and are often quarried for aggregates, for building stone and as a source of lime. Kelton and Knockmurton (NY 08 18), near Lamplugh, was the only large mine in the older harder rocks of the Lake District. There is also a cluster of small mines in granites near Boot in Eskdale (NY 00 17). Hematite very rarely occurs in coal-bearing rocks. A line of west to east faults separates the iron ore field from the West Cumberland Coalfield

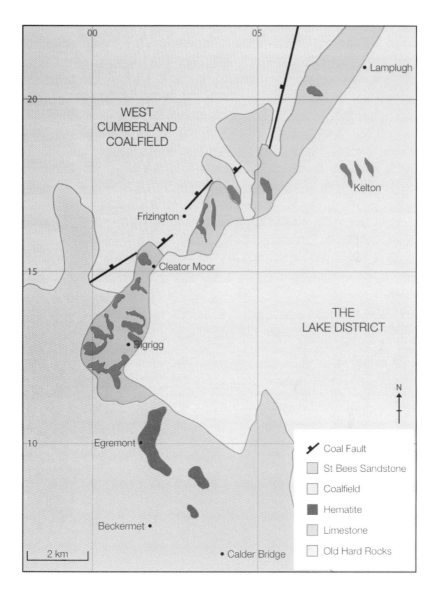

Figure 1. Map of the West Cumbria Iron ore mining area.

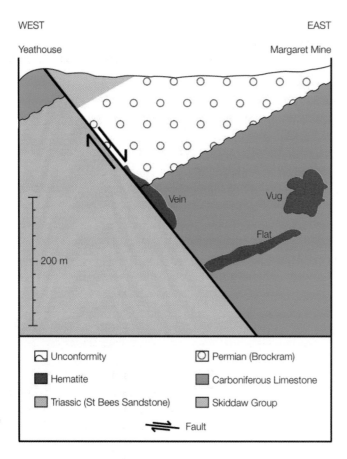

WEST   EAST

Yeathouse   Margaret Mine

200 m

Vein   Vug   Flat

Unconformity   Permian (Brockram)

Hematite   Carboniferous Limestone

Triassic (St Bees Sandstone)   Skiddaw Group

Fault

Figure 2. Diagram showing how hematite occurs.

The major ore-bearing rocks were found west of the granites of the Lake District. The iron ore is thought to have been deposited by hot fluids passing through the host rock, usually limestone. Deposits were common where there is or was a cover of permeable rocks, such as the red St. Bees Sandstone or the rocks locally called brockrams, which consist of very poorly sorted material including large angular cobble sized pieces. These permeable rocks allowed the ore-bearing solutions to pass through easily. The ore only occurred at or near to faults, usually on the downthrown side. Ore was rarely found below impermeable rocks like mudstone and shale, which the iron-bearing solutions could not penetrate easily. The coarser and more crystalline beds of limestone with their wide vertical joints and bedding planes accommodated the hematite more readily than the finer grained, muddy, limestone layers so more ore was found in the former.

Hot fluids brought in the hematite at around 80-120°C. These solutions were rich in oxygen and very salty, up to 6 or 7 times more saline than sea water. We don't know the source of the hematite. It could have descended from the surface or come up from great depths. Hematite in the limestones may have originated in overlying red iron-rich sedimentary rocks and percolated down into the limestones. This is thought to be the most likely source. Ores in the fissures near Kelton may have been carried up in hydrothermal (hot, mineral-rich) solutions from igneous rocks like the granites deep below the Lake District. When was the hematite deposited? We don't know! One suggestion is that it happened after the St Bees Sandstone formed, about 250 million years ago. This is the most commonly accepted idea. Evidence supporting this theory is that some of the faults carrying ore affect the St Bees Sandstone and that locally the St Bees Sandstone has been altered by the hematite. Another idea is that the ore was injected in Permian times (300-250 million years ago), after the Carboniferous Limestone had been deposited, but before the St. Bees Sandstone formed. The evidence supporting this idea is that there are hematite pebbles in some Permian age rocks, and these must have formed before the rocks in which they are found. Another line of evidence is from the rocks and ores at the Florence Mine. The hematite was weakly but permanently magnetized when it formed. This can be dated as we know how the earth's magnetic field has changed over time. As a result it seems possible that the hematite formed late in the Carboniferous or early in the Permian, well before the St Bees Sandstone.

Hematite is an iron oxide (Fe_2O_3). There are three main forms of the ore. The richest in iron is dense, very hard, brittle and a rather dull blue to black in colour. The greasy, much softer, less dense, earthy red ore is the least pure form worked. Intermediate in iron content are the more spectacular, dark red kidney ores which occasionally formed long pencil shaped pieces. These, like the much rarer dark, glittering, blade shaped crystals called specularite, are found in cavities in the ore body and near its edges. These cavities gave space which allowed the crystals of hematite to grow freely. Within the ore body are unwanted, non-metallic minerals, the "gangue". The most common is the very hard quartz (silica) with its pyramid shaped crystals. Other common gangue minerals are the softer calcite (calcium carbonate, often white or creamy) and dolomite (calcium-magnesium carbonate, often with creamy crystals shaped like crossed swords). Figure 3 is a photo of a vug, a natural space in which crystals can grow, in the roof of a gallery in Florence Mine (NY 10 01), Egremont. The ore is hard, very irregular and all too unpredictable in its occurrence, as shown on the map, Figure 1. It occurs in three main ways in West Cumbria, as illustrated in Figure 2. Veins are steep, narrow ore bodies close to faults; flats follow the rock layers, while vugs (also known as guts or loughs) have very irregular shapes. This unpredictability means that the ore is difficult and expensive to find and to mine. The initial method of searching for the ore is to look for the outcrops of ore-bearing rock and faults.

Figure 3. A vug in the Florence Mine.
Photo M. Dodd.

Boreholes (shafts) are then sunk to allow horizontal passages called levels and gently sloping drifts to be driven into the hard rock. Mining involved blasting at depths of up to 500m below the surface, initially using gunpowder but later dynamite. The mines needed expensive haulage and drainage systems. They remained unhealthy and dangerous.

Until 20 or 30 years ago large cauliflower shaped masses of kidney ore were often used as doorstops in many local villages. Sandstone doorsteps were often raddled or reddened using the softer ore. Many miners appreciated how attractive the crystals were. They made small wooden display cabinets with glass fronts to hold their prize specimens. One of these spar boxes is shown in Figure 4.

The kidney and pencil shaped crystals of hematite and the glittering crystals of specularite and a wide range of gangue mineral crystals are much sought after by keen collectors. Such specimens are on display worldwide in many national museums, as seen in the photo, Figure 5, taken in the Chicago Field Museum of Natural History.

Figure 4. Photograph of a Spar Box.
Photo F. Lawton.

Figure 5. Sample of specularite in the Chicago Field Museum of Natural History.
By courtesy of F. Lawton.

Chapter 2

The Rise and Fall
of Iron Ore Mining

The earliest known documentary record of hematite mining is probably a grant in 1134 by Alicia de Meschines, a member of the family of the Barons of Egremont, of an area near Clints Brow above Egremont. We believe this early mine was west of the A595, the Whitehaven-Egremont road, about 1km south of Bigrigg near Langhorn Farm (NY 002 126), see Figure 1. At that time iron ore was smelted using charcoal and burning very large quantities of wood. Most of the bloomeries which smelted the ore were in attractive Lakeland valleys which were well wooded then. Smithy Beck, Ennerdale (NY 122 148) is a well-known example. Hematite was very difficult to smelt as the process required high temperatures which were difficult to achieve by burning wood. The failed attempt by William Wood in 1728 to produce iron in blast furnaces at Howth Gill (NY 028 177) near Bleak House, Frizington illustrates this problem. The iron he produced was so poor that he had to leave the district in a hurry to escape from his very angry customers!

17th, 18th and 19th Century documents in the Record Office at Whitehaven tell of small hematite mines worked intermittently before the coming of the railways. Probably these were worked where the hematite occurred at the surface or in very shallow deposits. Documents indicate a mine was worked at Bigrigg more or less continuously from 1636 to 1701. Yeathouse Mine (NY 042 171) at Frizington, which was first leased in 1745, sent ore to Parton (NX 97 20) for export and to an iron works at Harrington (NX 98 25). Pack horses and possibly horse and cart would have carried this ore. When Tulk & Ley, a local firm, re-opened the Yeathouse mine in the 19th Century oak shovels tipped with iron were found, probably left by earlier miners – "the old men". There was increasing mining activity towards the end of the 18th Century, especially in Cleator Moor where Crowgarth (NY 016 153) was worked probably from 1753 and Jacktrees (NY 017 148) before 1797. Total output for the area was rising gradually at this time and reached around 100,000 tons per year by 1846.

The landowners did not normally work the mines. Usually they leased the mines for fixed terms to companies or individuals who took the financial risk and paid dead (annual) rent and royalties to the landowners who normally held the mineral rights.

Figure 6. Whinnah Pit, Lamplugh, about 1900. *By courtesy of the Lamplugh and District Heritage Society.*

Figure 7. (opposite page). Layout of a typical mine.

The Industrial Revolution with its growing use of steam power and its extensive railway building increased the demand for iron and steel. West Cumbrian ore mining expanded dramatically after the development of the Bessemer process in 1856 which made possible the cheap conversion of brittle pig iron into reliable quality steel. This process needed iron ore low in phosphorus and silica. West and South Cumberland had almost all the British reserves of non-phosphoric ore with as little as 0.005% phosphorus content. Cumberland iron ore dominated the market until just after 1878 when the Gilchrist-Thomas process was developed which allowed steel to be made using iron ores with a higher phosphorus content. The local West Cumbrian output boomed, reaching 1 million tons per year by 1870 and peaking at 1.7 million tons in 1882 after which it remained much the same until about 1918.

The new 19th Century mines were on the exposed ore field where the ore bearing rocks are immediately beneath superficial material (soil and unconsolidated rock) north of Egremont. There were then an immense number of shallow short-lived pits. Most mines had several pit shafts. Figure 6, shows a moderate size, well-organized pit, Whinnah, at Lamplugh in about 1900. An article in the Whitehaven News of March 2nd 1882 estimated that the Whitehaven, Cleator and Egremont railway was serving over 280 pits many of them very small. This railway dominated ore transport and was extremely prosperous paying annual dividends of over 10% for most of its existence. Its main competitor was the Cleator Moor to Workington line which opened in 1879. Another well-known railway was the "Baird Line" from Rowrah to Workington. Almost every mine of any size and most pits had their own dedicated branch line. Pits which did not have rail access used horses or in some cases overhead rope or cable ways to carry ore to an appropriate railhead.

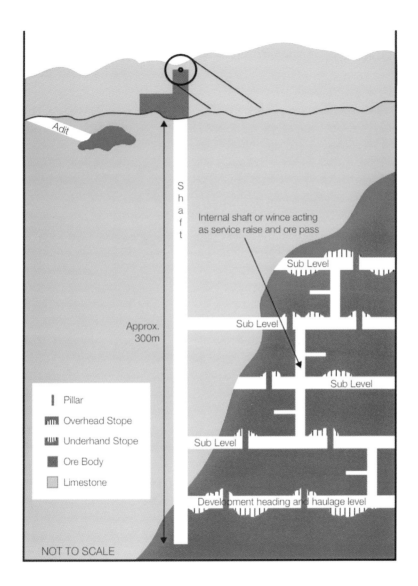

Adit

S
h
a
f
t

Internal shaft or wince acting
as service raise and ore pass

Sub Level

Approx.
300m

Sub Level

Sub Level

| Pillar

▥ Overhead Stope

▥ Underhand Stope

■ Ore Body

▨ Limestone

Sub Level

Development heading and haulage level

NOT TO SCALE

Iron ore is mined differently from coal as shown in Figure 7. Shafts are sunk *beside* not *into* the ore body. This is to avoid wasting any ore in the wall of the shaft. A level (horizontal tunnel) acting as a development heading is driven into the base of the ore body. Ore is then removed from the heading roof (overhead stoping) and from below the floor (underhand stoping). Internal shafts, sometimes called winces, which also act as service raises, are driven upwards.

Figure 8. A labourer emptying a 'modern' ore chute before 1980.
By courtesy of D. Powell.

Sub-levels are driven to access the ore and thirls, narrow horizontal passages, are hollowed out to improve air circulation. Pillars of ore or rock are left to support the roof. The ore obtained is usually dropped down ore chutes to the lowest or "horse" level from which it is lifted to the surface. Figure 8 shows one of these chutes. Adits which are gently sloping tunnels, also shown in Figure 7, are driven to reach shallow ore bodies. In the final days of working a mine, "robbery", the removal of the pillars to get as much ore as possible was common. Often this led to the collapse of the land surface.

Mining ore was dangerous. It was estimated that one in ten iron ore miners died during their working life due to mining accidents or mining related diseases. Roof falls were the most common cause of accidents. Other less frequent causes were shot firing accidents, floods, shaft accidents, being crushed by ore tubs and taking short cuts through dangerous abandoned workings. Table 1 below lists deaths in local iron mines in one year, 1879.

Person killed	Age	Name of Mine	Cause of Death
John Quayle	21	Parkside	Fell from cage
John Pool	30	Eskett	Roof fall
Lewis Hale	30	Eskett	Dynamite explosion
David Conway	18	Montreal	Roof fall in old working
Thomas Connor	42	Parkside	Roof fall
Henry Richards	25	Crossgill	Roof fall
Peter McVoy	26	Jacktrees	Roof fall
John Twigg		Salter	Fell from cage
James Hodgson	52	Crossfield	Shaft accident
William Fox		Cleator	Shaft accident
Thomas Graham		Salter	Roof fall

Table 1. Deaths in West Cumberland iron ore mines in 1879.

A later insidious problem, which often did not become apparent until after the miner had retired, was dust disease (pneumoconiosis) which was related to dry drilling of the rock. Neither the managers nor the miners were safety conscious. Drainage was often a problem. It was quite common for miners to drill through into other companies' workings to "pass on their water". Sometimes streams were diverted into impermeable tubes, metal boxes or concrete troughs to allow the ore below to be worked without flooding. Figure 9 on the following page shows such a feature at Parkside (NY 033 155) near Cleator Moor.

Figure 9. The metal box still carrying the Lingla Beck at Parkside near Cleator Moor.
Photo M. Dodd.

Industrial relations were very variable. Strikes and lockouts occurred. At first strikes almost always failed before unions became established. Common causes of unrest were disputes over wage rates and working conditions, especially in the early days when six day weeks of 10 hour shifts were the norm. Shifts of 8 hours became the standard as early as the 1880s though some firms tried to return to the 10 hour day. How the "company" system worked in individual mines often caused "local" disputes. Specific problems were personal and inter-union disputes.

By 1914 T. Gavan-Duffy of the Cumberland Iron Ore Miners and Kindred Trades Association negotiated on behalf of almost all the miners. His union had a very good name for financially supporting injured miners and their widows. After Gavan-Duffy died this union became part of the Municipal and General Workers Union which was said in the 1930s to be much slower in supporting individual miners and their widows interests and claims for compensation.

Population in the iron mining area rose dramatically in the middle of the 19th Century. Cleator parish had only 750 inhabitants in the 1840s but in the 1880s, there were more than 10,000 people there, mostly in Cleator Moor which had been the common land of Cleator. Similar growth took place in other settlements notably Frizington, Kirkland and Moor Row. There was huge immigration into the area, the best known being of Irish people into Cleator Moor. Cornish miners and their families moved into all the mining settlements almost 300 living in Kirkland in 1881. Most "incomers", however, were from other parts of what was then Cumberland. By 1880 the iron mines were employing over 6,000 men. Cleator Moor blast furnace (1842-1926) and foundries provided additional employment for men only.

Hurried house building, often unsafe and lacking services, accommodated this rapid rise in population. In 1857 six people died in Bowthorn Road, Cleator Moor after gas percolated from the slag heap on which the houses had been built. Similar disasters happened elsewhere. There was much violence in these new settlements. One example was the fighting at an Orange Order march in 1884 through staunchly Roman Catholic Cleator Moor during which one man was killed.

West Cumbrian mine managers and miners were slow to modernise, with high costs deterring investment. Development of the concealed ore field where the ore bearing rocks were below a great thickness of the red St. Bees Sandstone came later, in the 20th Century. Pits were sunk in this area at Ullcoats (NY 025 103) in 1901 and Beckermet in 1906, followed by Florence No.1 shaft in 1915.

Cheaper, lower grade ore from the East Midlands and good quality imported ore, particularly from Spain, took an increasing share of the UK market during the 20th Century. The coal strike of 1921 which paralysed the railways triggered the closure of most of the mines north of Egremont. Their failure had only been a matter of time as their reserves of ore were limited and their costs were very high. After the end of the coal strike output recovered briefly until the Great Depression of the 1930s. Thereafter annual output dropped below one million tons and the work force shrank to less than 2,000 men.

Even during the Second World War, when no foreign ores were imported and local employment prospects were better, output failed to recover. Gradually but erratically in the post-war years iron ore output and employment decreased until the last deep mines closed in 1980. The shallow Lonely Hearts lode (ore body) in the Florence Mine, (NY 01 10) produced small quantities of ore for making pigments and specialist castings until the nuclear industry ceased payments for pumping water out of the mine in 2007. Figure 10 is a photograph of the Florence Mine shortly before it closed in 2008.

Unemployment in the West Cumbrian iron mining area reached 60% in the 1930s. There were no jobs! Father Clayton, the parish priest at Cleator, organised voluntary work for the unemployed creating a grotto behind the Roman Catholic Church at Cleator in memory of Our Lady of Lourdes. This grotto is still visited by devout Roman Catholics. Ennerdale Rural District Council, the then local authority for the mining settlements, lost 20% of its population between 1921 and 1939. This massive outward movement of people was to the more prosperous South East of England. Earlier migrations had been much smaller and were often temporary. These were mainly skilled miners, with or without their families, who moved to newer mining districts in South Africa, Australia and North America. After World War 2 there was some recovery as people moved into West Cumbria when Britain became more prosperous and the nuclear industry developed.

Little now remains of the headgear and tips of the abandoned ore mines. Florence Mine still has its headgear and tips remain near Haile and at the Kelton Mine (NY 07 18) near Lamplugh. Subsidences have cast a blight on the area. Montreal School and the streets around it just west of Cleator Moor Square had to be demolished in the 1940s after being undermined by "robberies" in the Crowgarth/Leconfield Mine. Egremont is suffering today from shaft collapses near the West Lakes Academy (formerly Wyndham School). One subsidence, Longlands Lake (NY 01 12), was flooded after the local, shallow mines alongside the River Ehen were abandoned. This is now a much used recreation area and wild fowl wintering site. Today the mines and miners are remembered by a mural at Cleator Moor (see Figure 24) and by sculptures at Egremont but sadly there is no longer a heritage centre and no dedicated local museum.

Figure 10. Florence Mine. *Photo P. Carney.*

Chapter 3

Lamplugh and Kirkland

Lamplugh, at the northern edge of the iron ore field, has few remains of the old mines. A very small output of ore, about which little is known, was worked from near "The Cottage" (NY 079 217) between Lamplugh Crossgates and Mockerkin Tarn. This is probably the most northerly known supply of hematite in West Cumbria. Kelton and Knockmurton mines (NY 08 18), above Kirkland village were originally two separate mines but from 1868 were worked as one. Large tips and many subsidence hollows remain and are probably the most extensive traces of former iron mining in present day West Cumbria.

Lamplugh Mine was at the northern end of the limestones in which hematite was found and had several small pits sunk close to ore bearing faults. These pits, shown on the map, (Figure 11), were 100m or so west of A5086 beyond the pub, "The Lamplugh Tip", (NY 076 203) and extended approximately 300m north to south. They were active between 1880 and 1931. The early workings were near Murton Farm, then came Whinnah Pit which was near the road to Asby where the modern bungalows are today. Coronation Pit, whose remains lie behind the pub, was the last to open and was worked from 1910 to 1931. The pits were later connected underground and worked as one mine about 120m deep. An overhead ropeway carried the high-grade "blue" ores from these pits to Wright Green, the station for Lamplugh on the Whitehaven, Cleator and Egremont railway. Surprisingly, considering its remote position, this was one of the last mines in the north of the orefield to close in the 1930s. Its high production costs and small reserves made it uneconomic to continue working. Subsidence occurred as late as the 1970s along the road from Lamplugh Cross (NY 077 200) towards Lamplugh Church.

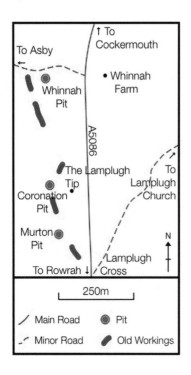

Figure 11. The Lamplugh Mine Area.

The joint Kelton and Knockmurton Mine was the only large hematite mine working in what is now the Lake District National Park. It produced 1.25 million tons of ore between 1852 and 1914. This mine was close to several faults in the sandstones and shales of the very old Skiddaw Group rocks. Its pit heads were at around 250m above sea level, far higher than any of the mines in the limestones. It worked 20 or more veins, usually steeply sloping, often of limited extent and varying greatly in width but in places bearing ore for lengths of up to 100m. These veins usually were narrow near the surface, widening at intermediate depths but generally pinching out by 200m depth. The map (Figure 12) locates the mine and the 5km long Rowrah and Kelton Fell Railway which opened in 1877 to carry ore to Rowrah station on the Whitehaven, Cleator and Egremont line.

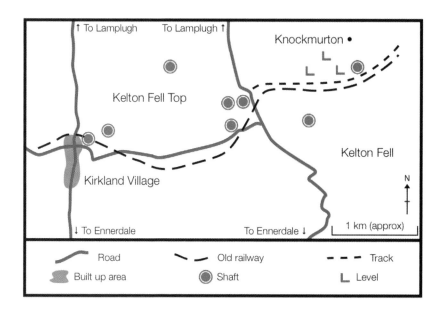

Figure 12. Map of Kelton and Knockmurton Mine.

Knockmurton was first worked in 1852, by Thomas Carmichael, in open cast diggings from the surface at over 300m above sea level. These were appalling working conditions even in "normal" West Cumbrian weather. The open cast location (NY 090 197) on Harris Side, Knockmurton, is shown on the photograph (Figure 13) as the hollow on the skyline climbing diagonally from right to left. In the foreground is the disused Rowrah and Kelton Fell railway. The photograph also shows red patches in the bracken which mark the position of adits, gently sloping passages into the fell. These adits, not shafts, accessed the veins, with one cut through to the Cogra Moss valley on the north of Knockmurton for drainage. Winces, which are internal shafts, were dug to work deeper veins. The photograph (Figure 14), of a sketch made from a water colour painted just after the mine closed, shows the Knockmurton mine layout.

Figure 13. Knockmurton Fell and the Rowrah and Kelton Fell Railway.
Photo P. Carney.

Figure 14. A contemporary watercolour of Knockmurton Mine about 1919. *Photo D. Powell.*

Figure 15. Teapot presented to William Ramsay.
Photo the Lamplugh and District Heritage Society.

The early years of mining were marred by a tragedy. On November 4th, 1854, Isaac Turner, a clerk carrying the miners' wages, was murdered between Ennerdale Bridge and Kelton. One of the miners he was due to pay, was arrested, tried, convicted and executed at Carlisle for the murder.

Work began at the much more productive Kelton Mine with the sinking of No.1 shaft to about 50m in 1873. Its tip, where small samples of ore and gangue minerals can still be found, is at (NY 084 181), just above the minor road east from Kirkland to the T-junction with the Lamplugh-Ennerdale Bridge road. Output was initially low due to the appalling state of the roads. Those from the mines to the Whitehaven, Cleator and Egremont railway were often impassable in winter. William Baird & Co, a large firm from Gartsherrie in Central Scotland, took over the leases in 1868 and worked Kelton and Knockmurton, which were connected underground, as one unit. A house was built in 1868 for William Ramsey, from Kilsyth in central Scotland, the first Knockmurton Mine manager, (1869-71). An unexpected link emerged recently. In 2007 the Lamplugh and District Heritage Society received a letter from a Mr Barnes in Christchurch, New Zealand, followed by photographs of a teapot he had bought at a local auction in New Zealand.

The teapot was inscribed

Presented to
Mr Wm. Ramsey
By the workmen of the Knockmurton Mines
As a token of respect
Lamplugh September 20th 1874

Figure 15 is a copy of one of the photographs of the teapot.

After the Rowrah and Kelton Fell railway from Knockmurton was opened in 1877 annual output increased dramatically, peaking at over 40,000 tonnes in 1888. Kelton Pits No. 2 and 3 were sunk to depths of about 100m and 180m as the Kelton ores were not economically accessible from horizontal adits. The ores were worked successively from levels served by No.1, No.2 and No.3 shafts in turn down to depths of 200m. Drainage adits were opened at about 50m and 125m down the slopes towards Ennerdale. In 1902, 121 men were employed underground and 20 on the surface. Ore was mainly extracted by overhead stoping, working from the bottom of the ore mass and "pulling down the roof". This was responsible for the hollows and lines of collapse on Cockan Farm land around (NY 085 184) which can be seen from the roads leading to Kirkland and Lamplugh. Figure 16 is a photo of one of these collapses. Kelton was abandoned in 1914 after the drainage pumps broke down. The ore was almost exhausted and pumping had become very expensive. A little work was done at Knockmurton until 1914 and again in 1923.

Figure 16. (opposite page). A collapse above a hematite vein at Kelton Mine.
Photograph P. Carney.

Kirkland village became the home of most of the Kelton iron ore miners. The 1881 census is a snapshot of boom times at the Kelton and Knockmurton mine. Of the 319 inhabitants with a Kirkland address then, 106 had been born outside what was then Cumberland and Westmorland. Of these incomers 31 had been born in Cornwall where the copper and tin mines were struggling, with 23 coming from Scotland and 16 from Ireland. Several were from the country districts of Cumberland and Westmorland. Miners' wages were distinctly higher than farm labourers' or the income from smallholdings or hill farms. There was even one person born in Russia!

Originally Kirkland had merely been a hamlet of a few farms and cottages but it had become a village by 1891. Table 2 below, which has been extracted from the censuses for Kelton township which Kirkland dominates, indicates the scale of the change. Many of the extra houses in 1891 were in 5 terraces built for the miners.

Year	No.of Houses	No. of inhabitants	Comments
1851	40	170	Mainly dependant on farming
1891	80	472	Mainly dependant on mining

Table 2. Extract from Censuses.

There was always the risk of fatal accidents and mine closures. At least 7 men were killed in the Kelton and Knockmurton mines before 1905. William Hope, a foreman at Knockmurton, who was possibly born in Lorton around 1849 married on a Sunday because he could not afford to miss a day's work.

The 1851 hamlet had a tailor, a dressmaker, a mason and a joiner. By 1891 the village also had a pub, a blacksmith, building businesses, a boot and shoe maker, a butcher, a painter and decorator, a shop and a grocery. The school, which is now called the Lamplugh Parochial School, opened in 1879 and had 120 pupils but only 2 teachers in 1883. The Primitive Methodist chapel, which closed shortly after 2000, was originally strongly supported by people from Cornwall. It opened in 1877 and was followed by the Kirkland Mission (Church of England) in 1886.

Chapter 4

The Frizington Area

Frizington was the poor relation in the parish of Arlecdon and Frizington, before iron mining developed. It was merely an area of poor farms on damp, sour soils. In 1851, just before the iron mine boom, the parish had a population of only 643. Iron ore output rose rapidly between 1860 and 1880 as did the population. At the 1881 census 6,586 people lived in the parish, mainly in Frizington! A long term decline followed. Many small mines closed before 1910 followed by the remaining bigger mines in the 1920s. The population of the parish dropped as a result to 4,328 in 1931 and only "bottomed out" at 3,422 on 1981.

There were two main groups of mines in the Frizington area. The most productive area was south of Frizington, near Parkside (NY 03 15). Here High House and Parkside mines dominated production which peaked about the 1860s. The other main group was further north, east of Frizington Main Street, which produced substantial amounts but not such large tonnages of ore as did the Parkside group. Its output peaked rather later. The Margaret and Lonsdale Mines (NY 04 17) were the biggest mines of the more northerly group. There were also many smaller, less productive and short lived pits between Parkside Bridge (NY 035 155) and the village post office (NY 034 172). Figure 18 on the following page, shows the location of the mines around Frizington.

Figure 17. A shift at Lonsdale Mine about 1900.
By courtesy of L. Davies.

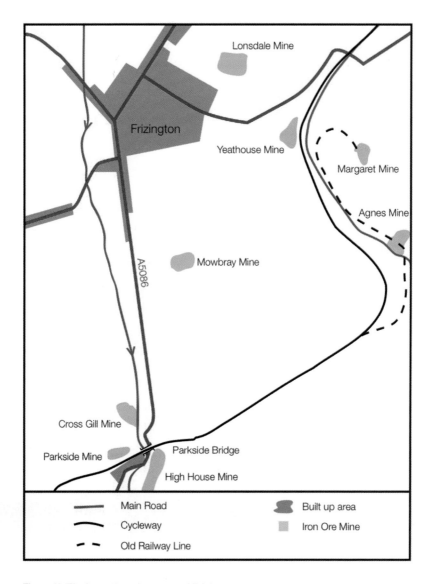

Figure 18. The hematite mines around Frizington.

Near Parkside a large mass of ore, a "flat", extended over an area of 25 hectares and was almost 20m thick. It was rather fancifully called the "El Dorado" of Frizington. This was in the topmost limestone, known as the 1st because it was the first the miners encountered as they dug down from the surface. It was worked at depths of about 100-200m or so. This limestone is about the same age as the Millstone Grit of the Pennines of which the textile mills of Lancashire and Yorkshire were built. It was richer in iron but the ore had more of the undesirable impurity, phosphorus, than that from deeper down in the thick, rather coarse 4th Limestone of the Eskett Limestone Formation, which was worked later. The High House Mine (1853-1905) was about 175m deep and was situated in the very wet ground across the A5086 in front and east of the Parkside Terrace of houses. It produced as much as 120,000 tons of ore in 1879, mainly from the large "flat". The much deeper Parkside Mine (1855-1925) was located just north of Parkside Terrace and the Whitehaven, Cleator and Egremont Railway. Parkside Mine worked the 4th Limestone beds, with its maximum output being in the 1860s.

Birks Mine with its prominent pond and vegetated tip was a small mine quite close to Parkside. This mine, originally an open cast, was flooded in 1894 when a new level which was being driven from No.7, the only shaft still open, drilled up into an abandoned working full of water. Two 15 year olds, Thomas Toye and Daniel Crone, together with 35 year old David Harrison were drowned. There were several other occasions when individual miners were killed in the Parkside area.

Subsidence was and is noticeable near Parkside, being responsible for the hollow area east of the A5086. The original High House farm building was demolished to allow more complete extraction of ore. Its replacement was built well above the High House Mine. Drainage was always a problem and a "metal box" was constructed to carry the Lingla Beck over the mine workings (See Figure 9). The Parkside Bridge shows the effects of subsidence over shallow workings as the upper and lower courses of brick and stone are not parallel. Subsidences often restricted traffic on the Whitehaven, Cleator and Egremont Railway.

The more northerly group of mines was quite close to the village but their workings caused little subsidence, because they were much deeper than the Parkside mines. These mines were at their busiest between 1880 and 1910. The Yeathouse Mine (NY 043 172), which was close to the Cycleway, was recorded as working in 1747. Its shallow workings in the lower limestones produced a little ore during the middle of the 19th Century before it closed in 1867. Lonsdale Mine (1879-1923) was about 250m deep and worked ore from several types of rock. Ore was extracted in small quantities from grits (coarse sandstones) and unusually from rocks that also contained coal all these being nearer the surface than the limestones. Most of the hematite came from the ore bodies in the many layers of limestone, output reaching a peak of 45,000 tons in 1904. The Lonsdale Mine's No. 5 pit (NY 143 177) was only about 200m from today's Community School. Despite its deep workings extending under the school and Main Street there has been no subsidence. Figure 17 is a photo taken about 1900 which shows a shift of some of the 180 or so men employed at Lonsdale.

The Margaret (NY 046 173) and Agnes Mines (NY 048 165) were further east between Windergill Beck and Windergill, in farmland about 1 km from the village. They were on the down-thrown easterly side of the big Yeathouse Fault (See Figure 2). Agnes was opened before 1850 and worked small reserves at shallow depths (100m or so) which led to considerable nearby subsidence. The original track of the Whitehaven, Cleator and Egremont railway line on the east of the Windergill valley had to be replaced by the route to the west passing by Yeathouse Station (on today's Coast to Coast Cycleway). A pipeline ("The Boilers") was installed to stop the Windergill stream water flooding the Agnes and Margaret mine workings beneath. The pipeline is shown in Figure 19. Countless generations of Frizington children have walked over or crawled through this, usually without their parents' knowledge! The rather overgrown area nearby has been very popular with teenage courting couples.

Figure 19. "The Boilers"
Photo. M. Dodd.

The Margaret Mine (1890-1923) was the last hematite mine to open in the area. It had only one shaft or pit, producing large tonnages of ore from the big deposits in the limestones under the much younger St. Bees Sandstone and the Permian breccia. This mine was 350m deep with a larger output (65,000 tons in 1913) than the much shallower Agnes Mine. Figure 2, shows how hematite occurred in the Margaret Mine. The original track of the Whitehaven, Cleator and Egremont Railway was reopened to serve the Margaret Mine. Closure came at the end of the lease when considerable tonnages of ore remained but there was no demand and prices were very low. The impact of the closure was so great that the *Whitehaven News* of October 4th 1923 asked , "What is to become of Frizington?"

A fatal accident in the Margaret Mine occurred on March 11th 1908, and is reported in issues Nos. 3 and 4 of the *Cumberland Miner*, the official journal of the Cumberland Iron Miners and Kindred Trades Association. William Cameron, a 37 year-old miner was buried below a rock fall in a robbery, where as much ore as possible was being extracted before the roof was allowed to collapse. It took 30 hours to recover his body. His death was not due to negligence! Later in July of that year his widow, who had three very young children, was allocated 8/- a week (£27.30 in present day (2009) money).

Although Agnes Mine ceased production in 1874 it was kept open. It was in daily use to pump water from the Margaret Mine and provided an essential alternative exit. This was the escape route for 27 men who were trapped underground on May 11th 1911 by what the *Whitehaven News* appropriately called a disastrous fire at the Margaret Mine which burnt down the mine headgear and put the mine shaft out of action. After normal pumping resumed the following morning the men emerged safely from the Old Agnes shaft. The Margaret Mine was closed afterwards for repair for about 3 months causing considerable hardship to the 300 employees and their families, most of whom lived in Frizington. The photograph of an old postcard, Figure 20, shows the scene then.

Figure 20. Postcard of Margaret Mine just after the fire of 11th May 1911.
By courtesy of L. Davies

34

It was not until the 1970s that the Margaret Mine shaft was capped. The considerable remains of the buildings had been a much used play area for Frizington children before they were demolished. It is now safely fenced off. There are some small remains of the Agnes Mine buildings, the possible site of a shaft, some retaining walls and an extensive ridge of clinker probably from inefficient coal fired boilers, all near the Windergill stream. The last mine chimney to survive was demolished in the 1990s when Eskett Quarry (NY 05 15) was extended. A rather frightening feature is the open trial or exploration entrance which was developed at the height of the mining boom. It is at most only 5m from the railway track just south of Yeathouse Station.

Almost all of the smaller mines were south of Frizington Post Office and north of Parkside Bridge on either side of the A5086. The Crossgill Mine (NY 034 158) west of the A5086 and the Mowbray Mine (NY 037 165) east of the A5086 were the only ones of moderate size. The Crossgill Mine (1855-1923) was over 300m deep and was said to have worked a thick ore body, probably part of the same large "flat" which was worked in the Parkside area. You can see from the main road (if you are not driving!) the remains of a mine working together with the overgrown ruins of a barrel-roofed dynamite hut, a circular pond and a small tip. A similar dynamite hut is shown in Figure 21. The Mowbray Mine (1865-1922) nearer to Frizington worked ores under Frizington Road houses, producing moderate tonnages from its 200m deep workings. East of the A5086 were several small mines with many pits about 150m at their deepest said to have been worked from as early as 1838 but all abandoned by 1907. This is now an area of very disturbed ground, overgrown small tips seeming to alternate with small steep sided collapses.

These small mines and their tips were excellent sources of mineral samples and specimens. The Dalmellington tip near the Crossgill Mine provided samples of the dense, brittle, glassy, tabular, yellow, pale green and pale blue varieties of barite. This pale blue variety of barite seems only to have been found in significant quantities around Frizington and Cleator Moor and was colourless until exposed to daylight. Good samples of the glittering black crystals of specularite were common on these small tips. In the Earth Science galleries of the Natural History Museum in London is a mass of kidney ore the size of an armchair which came from the (old) Parkside Mine, Frizington.

Figure 21. Ruins of a barrel-roofed dynamite hut.
By courtesy of L. Davies.

The early days before 1850

1831 Census. Population of parish of Arlecdon and Frizington was only 643.

1838 Yeathouse Mine reopened.

Several small mines north of Parkside Bridge opened before 1850.

The boom years, 1850-1880

Parkside area developed early:

1853 High House Mine opened.

1855 Parkside and Crossgill Mines opened.

1860-1880 Peak of production.

Bessemer Process for steel making was adopted at this time creating a huge demand for high quality hematite ores like those mined in West Cumberland.

Production from the area behind Main Street developed later and was rather smaller.

1850 Agnes Mine leased about this time.

1865 Mowbray Mine started.

1867 Lonsdale Mine opened about this time.

1881 Parish population reached 6,856 due to considerable immigration.

The long slow decline, 1880-1925

Newer steel making processes allowed the use of cheaper, less pure iron ores.

Most ore was mined east of Main Street.

1890 Margaret Mine opened.

1905 High House Mine closed.

1907 Most smaller mines had closed by this date.

1920s The larger mines closed, particularly after the 1923 Coal Strike.

1923 Crossgill and Margaret Mines closed.

1924 Lonsdale Mine, the last in the parish, closed.

Large-scale emigration to more prosperous parts of the UK.

1931 Population had dropped to 4328.

Afterwards

The remains of most of the mines were cleared by 1980.

1981 Drop in population "bottomed out" at 3422.

Figure 22. A Timeline for Frizington Mines.

Chapter 5

Around Cleator Moor

The Cleator Moor mines produced huge quantities of hematite from comparatively shallow depths, especially from the three main mines in the area, Montreal, Leconfield (which was also known as Crowgarth) and Crossfield. (See Figure 23).

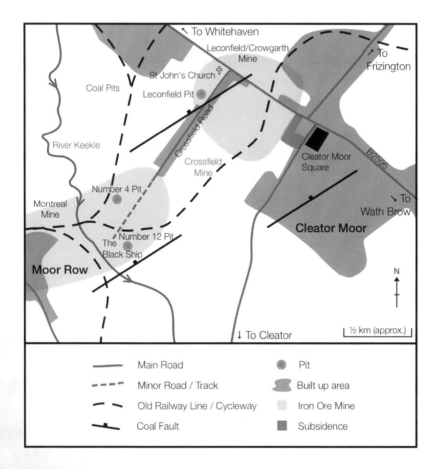

To Whitehaven

Leconfield/Crowgarth Mine

To Frizington

St John's Church ⊹

Coal Pits

Leconfield Pit ◉

Crossfield Road

River Keekle

Crossfield Mine

Cleator Moor Square

B2595

Number 4 Pit ◉

Montreal Mine

To Wath Brow

Number 12 Pit

Cleator Moor

The Black Ship ◉

Moor Row

N ↑

↓ To Cleator

½ km (approx.)

——	Main Road	◉ Pit
- - - -	Minor Road / Track	🗺 Built up area
⌢ ⌢	Old Railway Line / Cycleway	Iron Ore Mine
⊢⊣	Coal Fault	Subsidence

Figure 23. The Cleator Moor Iron Ore Mines.

The mines were not separate areas but consisted of a very confused jigsaw-like pattern of leases which led to many disputes over their boundaries. This was a far from efficient way to work the ore. Most of the mines were leased out to mining companies. Leconfield was the only mine where the royalty owner worked the pits and even there not until 1865, the height of the boom years. Like Frizington and Kirkland where the ore bearing rocks were also close to the surface, production boomed early between 1860 and 1880 but then declined. Few pits were still active after the 1920s. The heyday of hematite mining is commemorated by a mural, now sadly faded, and Conrad Atkinson sculptures behind the Library on Cleator Moor Square. Figure 24 shows the mural soon after it was painted.

Figure 24. Mural in Cleator Moor Square 1980s.
By courtesy of F. Lawton.

Montreal (1861-1925) was the richest of the local mines. It had at least 20 separate pit shafts almost all with their own branch line from the main railway. Some shafts mined coal north of the Coal Fault which is almost parallel to Crossfield Road. Figure 25 shows how Montreal No.4 Pit could mine both iron ore and coal. Montreal Mine's maximum output was the then enormous 2,250,000 tons of iron ore between 1871 and 1880 from pits on either bank of the River Keekle near Moor Row. The majority of the hematite was the very good, dense "blue" variety found in all the six limestones present in the mine. The thick 4th Limestone in particular hosted a great deal of ore. Several ore bodies were over 30m thick.

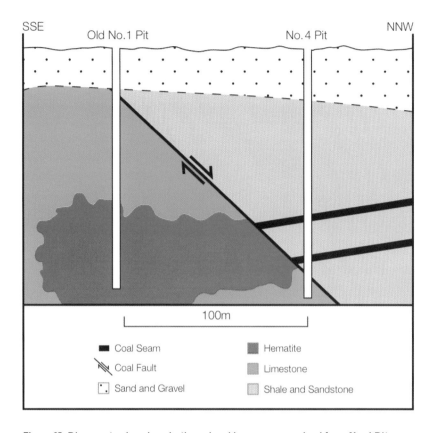

Figure 25. Diagram to show how both coal and iron ore were mined from **No. 4 Pit.**

41

A sandstone block (Figure 26) inscribed with a verse from the poem "Cleator Moor" written during World War II by Norman Nicholson now stands on the Coast to Coast (C2C) Cycleway at NY 009 146. This cycleway follows what was once the Whitehaven, Cleator and Egremont Railway.

Figure 26. Sandstone block inscribed with a verse from "Cleator Moor" by Norman Nicholson.
By courtesy of F. Lawton.

There is a modern artefact, a dramatic giant rock crusher with two very large blocks of stone alongside, on the site of Montreal No. 4 pit. Figure 27 is a photograph of this crusher.

Figure 27. (below). Abandoned rock crusher in 2009 on the site of Montreal Pit No.4. *Photo M. Dodd.*

Drainage was everywhere a serious problem. Accordingly the Stirling family who owned the Montreal Mines and their competitor, the Crossfield Company, had the River Keekle enclosed and "boxed". This is a concrete trough, the "Black Ship", which is about 500m long and 10m wide. Figure 28 shows part of the "Black Ship" as it was in 2009. Neighbouring mining companies were unwilling to contribute towards the maintenance of this trough, and threatened to sue if there were any damage caused by its drainage water into their mines. Montreal No. 12 Pit, of which there are some remains almost at river level, was the pumping shaft used to drain the Montreal Mine.

The Stirling family also worked a 5-10m thick deposit from a quarry and an opencast at Todholes. The deep hollow and vegetated tip left as a result of these workings became "The Big Hill" (NY 021 144), a playground for many Cleator Moor children.

Figure 28. The Black Ship. *By courtesy of F. Lawton.*

To reach Montreal No 4 pit and the "Black Ship", walk from Cleator Moor Square along B5295 for 400m or so towards Whitehaven. Turn left (south west) along Crossfield Road. Follow this gently sloping road for about 500m. The road becomes a lane after the last houses are passed. Montreal No 4 site is on the right hand side almost opposite a small stable and grazing area. Continue down this lane, which may become muddy, to the bridge over the "Black Ship" and the River Keekle.

The pits of the Leconfield/Crowgarth Mine were on either side of the B5295, the road to Whitehaven, between Cleator Moor Square and Crossfield Road. The Crowgarth Mine worked from around 1753 and was probably the earliest iron ore mine in the Cleator Moor area. It was the last to close locally in 1951 and was the main cause of subsidences in the 1940s. Its maximum output was over 77,000 tons in the 1870s. This was considerable, but much less than the Montreal Mine. Today (2009) Cleator Moor Co-operative Superstore is almost on the site of the Lord Leconfield Pit which was the pumping shaft for the Leconfield/Crowgarth Mine. Figure 29 shows this pit in 1917. Its ore bodies were in the upper limestones, in places immediately below the thick glacial drift and the coarse sandstones known as the Hensingham Grit. Most of the ore was of the hard "blue" variety. Some hematites from the York Pit (close to what is now the Cycleway) were pencil and kidney ore of jewellery quality. The later workings were south of the road to Whitehaven and had open chambers underground up to 20m in height. The maze of intricately connected workings were often no more than 30m below the surface. Equal weights of sand and mine water were pumped down to support the surface. This was said to be a successful but expensive way of preventing/delaying subsidence.

Figure 29. A 1917 postcard of Lord Leconfield's Pit, Cleator Moor.
By courtesy of L. Davies.

**Figure 30.
The Longlands Mine
in 1916.**
By courtesy of M. Moon.

The Crossfield Mine was south and west from Cleator Moor Square. It was worked between 1860 and 1919 and initially was very productive, producing almost 150,000 tons in 1874. However its ore bodies, which were in the lower, deeper limestones, were smaller, more difficult to work and not as high grade as those at the Montreal and Leconfield Mines. Its leases overlapped those of the Montreal Mine geographically and at different levels making working circumstances difficult. It was almost exhausted before 1900.

The Longlands Mine (NY 01 12) was one of the smaller mines but has made the biggest impact on today's landscape. It was active between 1879 and 1924 working thick flats in the bottom limestone which was only between 40m and 70m below the surface. This ore was of high quality with about 1/3 going to special steel works in Sheffield. Unfortunately it was in a wide stretch of the Ehen valley where unstable surface deposits of glacial gravels and wet river muds and sands were always likely to invade the mine workings. To reduce this risk a meander of the Ehen was removed after Jonas Lindow took over the lease in the 1890s and the Ehen was confined to its present day course. For safety's sake only one shift was worked per day. Figure 30, from page 212 of Caesar Caine's 1916 book *Cleator and Cleator Moor* is a view of the mine when it was still working. Near the southern edge of the present lake the remains of two pits, No. 1 illustrated by figure 31, and the almost overgrown No. 4, can still be seen. There are two railway bridges over the river, far more than you would expect for such a small mine.

Figure 31. Longlands No.1 Pit in 2009. *Photo P.Carney.*

Normally the landowner leased mining rights for a fixed period, charging a "dead (annual) rent" which had to be paid during the lease. Also royalties were charged on a sliding scale depending on the tonnages produced. The lease to Jonas Lindow of the Longlands mine in the 1890s for 25 years is a good illustration. The dead rent was £1,200 a year (over £88,000 in 2009 money). Normally royalties were to be charged at 1/6 of the ore price when the price was less than 12 shillings a ton (£42 in today's values) to 1/2 when ore was over £1 a ton (£67 in present day values). Lindow had the right to abandon the lease after 5, 10 and 15 years respectively. He was required to put the land back in good order at the end of the lease and would be charged for any permanent damage. Such provisions, common in leases, were impossible to undertake. When the lease was granted there was some limited subsidence near to what is now the eastern shore of today's lake. This lake, now known as Longland, only became permanent after the mine was abandoned in 1924.

The *Whitehaven News* published a long article about Stirling's Hospital on Jacktrees Road on October 5th 2006. This hospital was endowed by John Stirling, the owner of the Montreal Mine, in 1867, and included four beds for men injured in mine accidents. At that time it was the only hospital serving Cleator Moor and eventually closed in 1968 when the building became a private house. Patient records about the injuries suffered by miners make harrowing reading: John Musgrave, a boy of 14, was admitted with a spinal injury and stayed in hospital for 17 weeks in 1867. Hospital records for 1875 show 8 men were admitted following accidents in Montreal pits. In 1877, 23 year old Thomas Christian was caught between the cage and the opening of an abandoned gallery and was badly crushed. Sadly he died in hospital. In 1883, 15 year old Robert Poland fell down the shaft at one of the Montreal pits, thinking the cage was at the top of the shaft where he was working.

Other local mines were no safer. Dave Kelly in his book *The Red Hills*, published in 1994, mentions loss of life in the Cleator Mine which was owned and run by the Ainsworth family. Three men were suffocated in a drift entrance in 1888 and William Currie died in November 1889 from injuries sustained in a roof fall. At that time working conditions in iron ore mines were far less regulated than those in collieries. The deposits at the Cleator Mine were small and difficult to mine so the output was never large.

The Whitehaven, Cleator and Egremont Railway served Cleator Moor from 1856 and is now part of the Coast to Coast Cycleway, is reached from the dip in Leconfield Street, 200m from Cleator Moor Square towards Whitehaven. Figure 32 on the following page, shows one of the attractive Coast to Coast waymarkers on this route. A more northerly branch line serving Montreal No.4 Pit and Bowthorn was opened in 1866. Later this railway company came under the control of one of the larger national networks the London & North Western which raised freight charges substantially. The local mine owners combined to finance the building of the Cleator to Workington line with its Keekle Viaduct which opened in 1882 and operated till 1923. It then became part of the London, Midland and Scottish Railway and, later, British Rail. The Keekle Viaduct was eventually closed to freight traffic in 1963. Railway closures were inevitable when the mines, their main sources of traffic, closed from 1923 onwards.

CLEATOR MOOR
FRIZINGTON
ARLECDON
ROWRAH
KIRKLAND

PUBLIC FOOTPATHS
JACKTREES ROAD
CROSSFIELD

48

Subsidences have afflicted the area although the only recent one appears to be part of the old viaduct over the River Keekle, which was showing signs of collapse in April 2009. The 1940s were the time of the worst subsidences when Montreal and St. Patrick's Schools and the surrounding streets immediately northwest of Cleator Moor Square had to be abandoned as they were undermined by workings in the Crowgarth Mine. Hematite was found at the top of the rocks immediately under the thick glacial drift below the surface. Workings were so close to the surface that the miners could hear the Montreal School clock striking and housewives knew when to put the potatoes to boil for their miner husbands' evening meals after noises from underground stopped! Shot firing underground at the end of a shift often rattled crockery and fire irons in houses above the mine. Mine workings at safe depths underlie nearly all Cleator Moor west and south of the B 5205, such as the Jacktrees and Todholes areas but there are no reports of recent subsidences, or any apparent risks. Health and Safety issues mattered very little in the boom years. In 1871 a collapse, 30m deep and 50m wide, close to Crossfield No. 2 pit opened up on the Whitehaven, Cleator and Egremont Railway line not long before a passenger train was due!

In 1841 Cleator Moor was part of the parish of Cleator, being largely the Common land of Cleator with a few small patches of enclosed farmland. The parish population then was 761 but rose dramatically as a result of the mining boom to 9,464 in 1891, mainly in the new settlement of Cleator Moor. Population declined during the twentieth century as the mines closed and unemployment (male) reached 60% in the hard times of the 1920s and 1930s. The population of Cleator Moor dropped by over 20% from 8291 in 1921 to 6581 in 1931. Roman Catholic priests at Cleator had notebooks listing the many homes where the wife was the head of the household with the husband seeking work in more prosperous areas. Population decline is still continuing, dropping from 7270 in 1991 to 6760 in 2001, little more than in the depths of the Great Depression of the 1930s.

Figure 32. A waymarker on the Coast to Coast Cycleway.
Photo M. Dodd.

Chapter 6

Egremont and Beyond

Egremont is a far older settlement than Cleator Moor or Frizington. It became a market town just below Egremont Castle, the home of the Lords of the Manor, the de Meschines family, early in the 12th Century. In 1841, just before iron ore mining developed in West Cumberland, its population was 1,750. This rose to 5,976 in 1881 at the peak of the mining boom in Cleator Moor and Frizington. Egremont was less affected by the Great Depression of the 1930s than settlements to the north with 6,017 people living in the parish in 1931, only about 300 fewer than in 1921. Work was continuing in the big, more modern iron ore mines to the south of Egremont. The Beckermet Mine the largest of the modern mines reached its maximum annual output of 300,000 tons in 1929, almost at the depth of the depression. By 2001 the population of Egremont was 7,990 a drop of around 3% since 1991.

Large scale iron ore mining began around 1870, about 20 years later than in Cleator Moor and Frizington. It ended when the Beckermet Mine, the last of the deep mines, closed in 1980. There were two very different types of mine in the Egremont area, separated by a fault which runs north-west to south-east near the northern end of the town bypass. North of the fault and underlying most of Egremont were several shallow mines in the limestone beneath glacial deposits. See Figure 33. These mines were active between about 1875 and 1924 when the Coal Strike led to their closure. South of the fault there were a few, very much bigger and deeper mines sunk through the thick red St. Bees Sandstone which covered the ore bearing limestones. These deep mines were worked from around 1900 until 1980, when their local market, the Workington Iron and Steel plant, closed. The closure of Beckermet Mine ended large-scale iron ore mining in West Cumbria and was the death knell of its associated, very individual culture and way of life.

In both types of mine iron ore occurred in two quite different situations, illustrated in Figure 34. One was in vertical masses, "veins", following some of the faults. The other was in "flats", horizontal masses in the lower limestones, just above the Lake District rocks of the Skiddaw Group of sandstones and shales which come to the surface in the Western Fells.

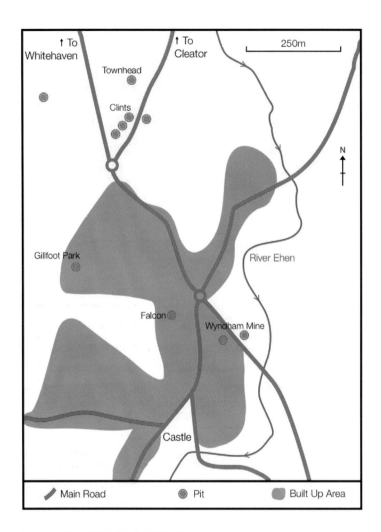

Figure 33. Map of the Egremont Mining Area.

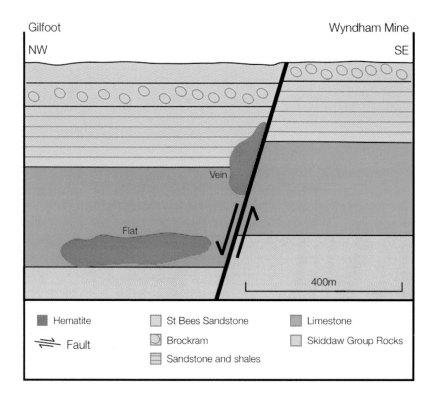

Gilfoot

NW

Wyndham Mine

SE

Vein

Flat

400m

▨ Hematite	▢ St Bees Sandstone	▨ Limestone	
⇌ Fault	▢ Brockram	▢ Skiddaw Group Rocks	
	▤ Sandstone and shales		

Figure 34. A cross-section to show how hematite occurs under Egremont.

The mines under Egremont extend southeast in a line from Gillfoot Park under the Smithfield housing estate, the West Lakes Academy site, Main Street and the Co-op Supermarket almost to the River Ehen. E.A. Read in *Discovering Egremont* (1992) stated it was possible between 1871 and 1895 to walk underground from Gillfoot Park No.1 pit to Wyndham No.2 pit close to the River Ehen as shown on the map, Figure 33. He also wrote in *Discovering Egremont* "When all the local mines were working the River Ehen ought to have been called the Red River for it ran hematite red (blood red) six days a week carrying all the water pumped from the pits."

The Gillfoot Park Mine had several pits raising ore from about 250m. Its maximum output was around 120,000 tons in 1889. There was a strike there in 1884 when the management tried to extend the length of shifts from eight to ten hours. Sadly this mine had many fatal accidents. The small, 200m deep Falcon and Lonsdale mines continued the line from Gillfoot Park to the Wyndham Mine which was between Main Street and the River Ehen. Wyndham Mine first produced ore in 1878 from pits less that 150m deep and its output peaked at about the same time as that of Gillfoot Park. Its Pit No. 2 was flooded by the River Ehen in 1890. Gillfoot Park Mine laid off 80 men in the same year when there was a recession in the iron and steel industry. The Wyndham Mining Company took over the Gillfoot Park and Falcon Mines in 1901.

The ore quality in the mines under Egremont was rather variable and any reserves accessible when these mines closed were very limited. Drainage was a continuing problem. Whether this is true is very uncertain, but it is said that 60% of the ore under Egremont has been left in pillars to prevent the collapse of overlying buildings. E.A. Read wrote in *1000 Years of Egremont* in 1999 "The town stands on pillars left to support the workings, workings now filled with water".

Another small group of mines, Townhead and Clints, was just north of the roundabout where the roads to Whitehaven and Cleator meet. One of their small tips is still visible. Both these mines were relatively shallow, producing small amounts of high-grade hematite. Townhead was the scene of a flood disaster in March 1913 when three men were trapped underground for five and a half days. One man was drowned. The other two, John Cairns and James Ward, survived. A three-inch borehole gave them fresh air. Food, hot drinks, warm clothes and candles were lowered down that borehole until the water was pumped out of the 70m level in which they were marooned.

Subsidences have long affected Egremont. Unfortunately they are still happening and likely to recur. The most recent was in June 2005 when part of the capping of Gillfoot No. 6 pit collapsed in the garden of a pensioner's bungalow (See Figure 35). As a precaution the bungalow was vacated. Part of the hard surfaced play area of the West Lakes Academy is covered with green algae, lichen and moss due to a less dramatic subsidence of the Falcon Mine which has also affected what was the tennis court area. E.A. Read in *Discovering Egremont* writes "The whole of the Smithfield Estate... was built on land known to be undermined... many of the mine workings are only 100 feet below the surface". Figure 36 shows a small, water filled hollow east of the road to Cleator which is a collapse of the Ehen Mine, part of the Townhead-Clints group. Perhaps the most gruesome incidents were the collapses of graves in part of the Egremont Cemetery above the very shallow Whin pit in 1879 and 1880. A later court action led to the closure of that pit in 1882.

Figure 35. The collapse of Gillfoot No 6 Pit, June 2005. *Photo West Cumbria Mines Research Group.*

Figure 36. The Ehen Mine collapse near Egremont. *Photo H. Carney.*

The deep mines south of Egremont worked ore in the comparatively thin lower limestone beds below a 300m cover of red St Bees Sandstone. At the Florence Mine the ore bearing rock rests on Skiddaw Group rocks like those of the northern fells. At Beckermet they rest on Borrowdale Volcanic Group rocks similar to those forming the famous rock climbs of the central Lake District. As the map in Figure 37 shows the ore field was extensive, stretching from the Florence Mine in the north almost to Robertgate Bridge near Calderbridge in the south. Unfortunately the ore bodies were not continuous but a complex area of flats and veins which all too often unpredictably narrowed or disappeared. Initially these ores were extracted from three separate mines, Beckermet, Florence and Ullcoats, and were not worked as a unit until 1970.

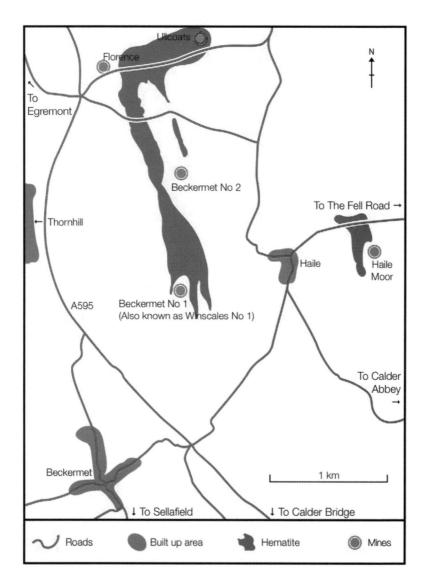

Figure 37. The deep mines south of Egremont.

Ullcoats Mine was worked between 1900 and 1968. It was situated below the very wet Black Moss and mined ore almost at the base of the lower limestones under glacial drift, the pebbly brockram and St Bees Sandstone. Although 3 of its 7 shafts had to be abandoned due to sand and gravel incursions it produced as much as 140,000 tons in 1906.

Figure 38. A drift at Florence mine in the 1990s. *Photo M. Dodd.*

To get as much ore out as possible, the 'mansion' of the same name was demolished. Ullcoats Mine was linked for the last twenty or so years of its working life, at a shallow depth with Florence Mine. Both mines worked the same ore body. Florence No. 1 shaft was sunk in 1914 through the ore body which prevented the working of much good ore. A second shaft was sunk in 1940 to extract more ore. Its 300m deep levels were abandoned in 1980. Small-scale production continued from the shallow (40m) Lonely Heart lode until March 2008 when water levels rose after the nuclear industry ended its payments for pumping. In the last ten years or so the Lonely Heart lode was reached by foot along a drift (seen in Figure 38) as the shaft lost its licence for man-riding. This meant that men could not descend in the shaft cages. "Vugs" in the roof of the lode had spectacular displays of kidney and specular ore (see Figure 3), besides highly saleable and rather unusual calcites and fluorspars. The small output of ore was used for moulds for casting and for pigments.

The highly productive but in places rather dangerous Haile Moor Mine above the village of Haile was close to the fells at 150m above sea level. It worked ore bodies inaccessible from Beckermet Mine. The ore it mined was carried by aerial ropeway to Beckermet No. 1 shaft – see Figure 39. It was worked from 1939 until 1973 from two levels off a 250m deep shaft. These mines could only be worked efficiently and safely after the development of large scale powered machinery with regular investment in more modern equipment. Beckermet No.1 pit shaft, initially sunk between 1903 and 1906 to 350m, was deepened between 1912 and 1915 to over 400m before being completely re-equipped in 1946. Haile Moor Mine, sunk in 1939 and the last iron ore mine to open, was one of the first mines in the country to have electrically operated winding gear (See Figure 40). Powerful underground pumping stations were essential. Those at Beckermet Mine were capable of raising 3,800 gallons per minute, necessary because the glacial gravels near the surface and the upper beds of St Bees Sandstone were major water bearing horizons. These more modern shafts carried high voltage power and compressed air lines for operations underground. They also provided much safer man riding and ore haulage cages.

Figure 39. The aerial ropeway near Haile Moor Mine. *By courtesy of D. Powell.*

Figure 40. Electric winding engine at Haile Moor Mine in 1950s.
By courtesy of D. Powell.

To prevent or minimize the effects of roof falls in areas with poor roof conditions heavy duty H section arched girders were used together with steel mesh and corrugated sheeting as shown in Figure 41. These precautions were also employed when driving new headings. Accidents were fewer as result but even so on 4th July 1953 four men were killed in Beckermet Mine by a roof fall when drilling a new heading. They were James Bailiff (a deputy), George Cromwell, George Wilson Cromwell and an Italian immigrant.

Figure 41. Roof reinforcements at Haile Moor Mine. *By courtesy of D. Powell.*

Compressed air drills mounted on pneumatic air-legs replaced much physical hard work for the miners (See Figure 42). Expensive remote electric shot firing was used for safety's sake in difficult areas as shown in Figure 48 in Chapter 7. Usually the cheaper but more dangerous safety fuses and detonators remained the norm. Bulk transport on main roadways of ore and material was by electrically operated trolley locomotives with attached cable reels for remote haulage. Battery operated locomotives were used in development headings. Figure 43 shows bogies on the surface at Florence Mine for use underground. Where possible ore was loaded mechanically. A remotely controlled motorized shovel loading ore from a development heading is illustrated at work in Haile Moor Mine in Figure 44.

From top:

Figure 42. Bill Kilgour and Ike Wilson drilling a development heading after 1945.
By courtesy of D. Powell.

Figure 43. Bogies used underground at Florence Mine.
By courtesy of D. Powell.

Figure 44. Ken Drinkwater operating a motorized shovel to load ore.
By courtesy of D. Powell.

Figure 45. Loading ore at Beckermet No 1 Pit. *By courtesy of D. Powell.*

A conveyor belt carried ore mined near Beckermet No.2 shaft to Beckermet No.1 for haulage to the surface for loading by gravity into railway wagons as shown in Figure 45.

These changes increased the output per man and reduced some of the risks of working underground but there was still hard physical work, often in hot, dusty and noisy conditions, for the smaller work force needed. Manhandling bogies and large quantities of material, both on the surface and underground, was still common in the 1950s. Pit head baths were not installed near Beckermet No.1 shaft until the 1950s. The labour force decreased considerably at Beckermet from over 800 in 1923 to about 275 in the early 1950s as output dropped to less than 150,000 tons. The opening of the Sellafield nuclear plant in the 1950s cushioned the long continued, gradual loss of jobs in mining. The higher wages and greater security of employment at the nuclear site led to a shortage of labour at the mines. This was overcome by recruiting workers from the north of Italy during the 1950s.

Figure 46. The Wheel at Florence Mine. *Photo P. Carney.*

Exploration for ore bodies was normally carried out by deep drilling from the surface along a grid of boreholes. In 1947 The United Steel Company decided to experiment with some of the then new geophysical methods for locating the hematite or the faults which carry it. Magnetic and electrical methods were unsuitable as hematite is essentially non-magnetic and non-conducting. A gravity traverse failed to locate any hematite. Seismic refraction was tried. Unfortunately the contrasts in seismic velocity through the different rocks was less than the margin of error and seismic refraction was a failure, unable to locate even accurately known faults let alone ore bodies.

Florence No.2 Pit cage and winding wheel shown in Figure 46 are the only large remains of the headgear of the mines. Beckermet No.2 site was cleared while Beckermet No.1, Ullcoats and Haile Moor sites were designated as industrial estates. Their lack of services and remoteness led to these industrial estates failing.

After the Second World War the demand for West Cumbrian hematite gradually decreased. The ore bodies were deep below the surface, relatively small in size, hard to work with inevitably higher costs than recently developed ore fields in Australia, Brazil and eastern Canada. These have far larger ore bodies on or near the surface and of higher grade. Thus they are much cheaper to work as they are largely quarried or opencast. As long as present circumstances continue it seems very unlikely that iron ore will ever be mined again on any significant scale in West Cumbria.

Chapter 7

The "Red Men" and their memories

by Maureen Fisher

This record of iron-ore mining would not be complete without a mention of the men who toiled to produce the ore. Small time farmers who owned land became rich beyond their wildest dreams once the ore was discovered on their land. Communities grew almost overnight with men and their families travelling, sometimes on foot, from every part of the British Isles to secure employment in the mines. This dirty, dangerous work was, for many, better than trying to eke out a meagre existence on poor, unproductive farmland. In much of West Cumbria the way of life changed from rural to industrial in a very short time, partly due to the effects of the Enclosure Acts, which deprived many small farmers of their traditional common grazing land.

Some of our small Cumbrian villages resembled the shanty towns which had evolved during the gold rush in the Yukon with a wide range of cultures and creeds. It was said that the roadways ran like blood as the iron-ore dust mixed with the mud and wet on the then unmetalled surfaces. Women had to hoist up their skirts in order to walk the streets. Water supplies were intermittent until reliable pumps were installed and sewage systems were non-existent with the "Night Soil Man" collecting the waste from the dry closets possibly shared by two or three families. Housing might be provided by the mine owners and private landlords and varied in its quality and facilities. Miners and their families regularly faced the threat of eviction if production at the mine slowed down and men were paid off.

A hard life, exhausting work, in a strange place, unfamiliar dialects, far from home and family - what plucky pioneers those early miners were. Their descendants should be justifiably proud of their forbears.

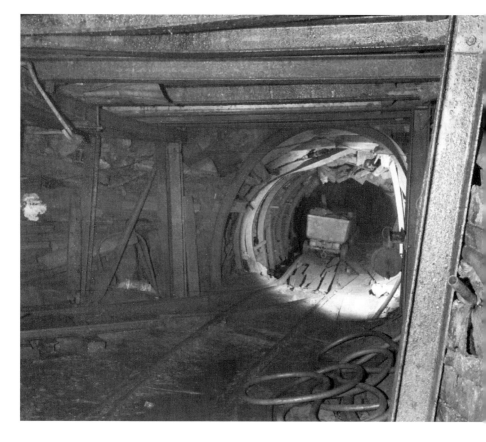

Figure 47. Roof conditions at Haile Moor Mine in the 1950s.
By courtesy of D. Powell

The Work

Men usually began work down the mines as labourers. They worked as part of a team or "company". Early in the month the team leader, who was usually an experienced miner, was responsible for working out a "bargain" or contract with the mine manager for the next section of ore to be taken out – "a spot". The price of the "bargain" depended on the amount and nature of the rock which needed to be drilled through to get to the ore and the amount of timber roof supports which would be required. Figure 47 shows difficult roof conditions in Haile Moor Mine in the 1950s. The miners themselves had to buy supplies for working underground including explosives, fuse wire, candles, and timber for pit props, from the management. The yardage and tonnage were also estimated with the Deputy in charge of measuring. He had to account for every inch so he made sure that anyone assisting with the measurement didn't try any crafty manoeuvres, such as winding the tape measure around their hand to attain a few extra inches.

Figure 48. Alf Verroa firing a shot at Haile Moor Mine in the 1950s.
By courtesy of D. Powell

In the early days the manager paid the full amount to the team leader, who then paid the labourers and boys. In later years workers were paid directly by the company according to their particular job. In the late 1950s this amounted to £5 per week on the surface and £6 underground after six weeks training.

One of the most dangerous occupations was that of Shot-Firer. His job was to drill a hole, into which was placed the explosive attached to the fuse. The fuse was lit by carbide lamp and it was a case of ensuring it was alight and then making a quick dash for cover. Calm nerves were required especially if the fuse didn't light first time. Safety improved with the introduction of remotely controlled electric firing. Figure 48 shows Alf Verroa, Under Manager at Haile Moor Mine firing a shot. Miners often worked in the same team and with the same work-mate for many years at a time. They came to trust and rely on each other.

Much of the drilling and shovelling took place in very wet conditions. It was not unusual for a miner to be drilling into rock and water to be pouring in on him as he worked. In more recent times miners working in these conditions wore oilskins throughout their shift, which was half an hour shorter than the normal eight hours. Drilling in such conditions is shown in Figure 49.

Early miners wore old clothes, which sometimes had to be dried on the oven door at home overnight if they had been working in a wet area. Some wore woollen singlets (bought at Collis's pawn shop in Whitehaven), woollen socks, which were often more darn than sock and heavy clogs. Protective clothing and changing facilities with showers were introduced, especially during the 1950s.

The changing rooms had "clean" and "dirty" areas. When starting work the miner took off his clothes in the "clean" area, fastened them to a pulley and hauled them up out of the way of dust and water. He then went into the "dirty" area where he pulled down his work clothes using a similar pulley system. Boots, clogs and shoes were kept in compartments under the benches. For some reason boot laces were always going missing – a cause of great annoyance to young miners until they learned that a good alternative to boot laces was the outer casing stripped from the fuse wire – as long as the mine manager didn't find out!
During the Second World War miners received a bar of Carbolic soap and could purchase towels "off the ration". They were also issued with a quarter pound of Typhoo tea every week.

Toilet facilities could be very basic. At Knockmurton Mine they consisted of old tar barrels. After much protest, two old dilapidated railway carriages were brought into use but concern was raised in the January 1908 edition of "*The Cumberland Miner*" that this new facility may develop in the minds of the men an insatiable desire for travel. The article continues, "The men may sit cosily in the corner of their railway carriage changing house and think they are on their holidays."

Figure 49. Angelo da Crema and Carlo Lamberi drilling in wet conditions.
By courtesy of D. Powell.

Snacks or "bait" were eaten underground. They usually consisted of sandwiches (not meat as it was thought to "go off" underground) or cold pasties. Cold tea was carried in a tin flask. This was often warmed by slotting the flasks between three nails fixed to a plank of wood attached to the wall. Underneath this plank was another, on to which were placed lit candles under each flask. Because the mines were often close to farms, it was possible to have a pint of milk delivered underground.

News travelled fast down the mine. For example, in the event of a national disaster, or the death of a member of the Royal Family or the result of a very important football or rugby match, a note would be pinned to a bogey which would reach the majority of the work force in due course. The miner was very often able to amaze his family, when he got home, with up-to-date news after being underground all day.

The work was not without its dangers and stories of injuries and death abound. There are also accounts of acts of bravery and heroism such as took place at the Margaret Mine at Frizington in July 1918. A roof fall occurred while three men, James Fisher, Robert Saville and Robert Kenmare were engaged in putting timber into a working. Robert Kenmare escaped unhurt but the other two remained trapped. A rescue party consisting of Alfred Horn, John Joseph Nevin, Joseph Adams, Tom Hutchinson, Henry McDonald, John Pepper, Thomas Saville and William McManus (Deputy) managed to extricate the trapped men despite the constant danger of large rocks falling from the roof. Robert Saville was found to be badly bruised but no bones broken. Unfortunately James Fisher was more seriously injured and died later in Whitehaven Infirmary. All were awarded an honorary certificate and their names added to the Carnegie Hero's Fund Roll of Honour which was established by the industrialist and philanthropist, Andrew Carnegie, in 1908. Six of the men were given £5 each but Mr Horn and Mr Nevin were given £10 each and attended Buckingham Palace to be awarded the Edward Medal by King George V.

Prior to the formation of trade union associations and compensation schemes for industrial injuries coming into operation, the miners received no financial help from the mine owners should they be unfit for work for any reason other than injury. The only help came from the parish or in some areas, such as Lamplugh, "Friendly Societies" were set up into which the miners paid a regular contribution and from which they received a small sum to tide them over in the event of illness or redundancy.

By the early 1900s the *Cumberland Iron Ore Miners and Kindred Trades' Federation* was in operation with active branches or lodges in most towns and villages involved in mining. A glimpse into their procedures, recorded in *"The Cumberland Miner"*, the union journal, edited by T Gavan-Duffy, gives us an indication of the struggle of the miners to secure a minimum living wage and safer working conditions. Reports of accidents and inquests and claims for compensation are interspersed with a smattering of poetry and humour. One such story describes an enquiry into the efforts of Frizington Council to supply the village with gas for the householders and also for street lighting. This proposal was apparently met with some opposition from the mine owners because the article continues in satirical mode:-

> *".......Iron Ore miners, walking through the beautifully laid out footpaths, inhaling the sweet morning air in mid-winter at 4am, are actually expecting to have their way lighted up – the cheek of them! Why, the next thing they will be wanting is ashes strewn on the footpaths so that they won't slip and break their necks – the beastly extravagant creatures!"*

The writer proposed an alternative to the scheme which was to let the miners stay in bed during the winter months until the same hour as those who opposed the gas lighting scheme, then they wouldn't need light.

Home life

Perhaps the following lines give an insight into the lives of the families of the iron-ore miner of the 19th century:-

> An t'lads, to be shoor, sec seets they com heamm.
> Wi' sec cleaz, an sec feasses, it was a fair sheamm:
> An' than they meadd t'blankets far worse nor git oot,
> For they leukt for o't warld like webs o' reed cloot.

From 'The Crack of an Ore- carter's Wife' by William Dickinson

Apart from describing the distress of the ore carter's wife as she recalls how dusty and dirty her menfolk are on returning from work, this poem is written in Cumbrian dialect which must have seemed like a foreign language to the many who came from other parts of the country. The wife goes on to bemoan the fact that the bed clothes become stained with the red ore and her thoughts must dwell on the unenviable task of getting them and the miner's work clothes clean.

The harassed housewife at that time would have no running water; every drop had to be carried from the pump and heated up on the fire for washing purposes. The alternative was to light a fire under the boiler or "set-pot" which might be outside in the yard and shared with her neighbours. It took gallons of water and elbow grease followed by many rinses in a variety of tin baths and dolly tubs before the articles could be described as reasonably clean, or at least free from dust, although they would always retain the tell-tale shade of pink from the iron ore. The same treatment could also be applied to the poor iron ore miner but, it is said, that despite all that washing and indeed for some time after retirement, their sweat was still tainted with the red ore dust. They described it as "being in their blood".

If trying to keep the house clean was one problem, feeding a large growing family was another. Many miners supplemented the family's diet by growing as much as they could on allotments, or for the more fortunate, in their gardens. This led to the setting up of gardening clubs and horticultural societies.

Table 3 (overleaf) shows where incomers to Lamplugh Parish were born.

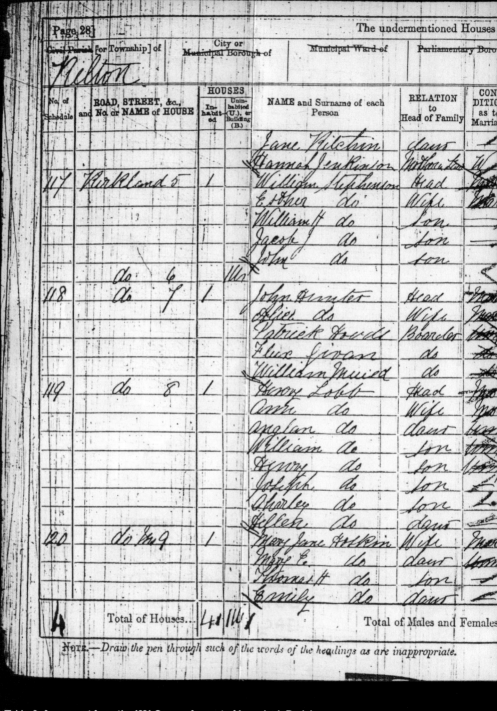

No. of Schedule	ROAD, STREET, &c., and No. or NAME of HOUSE		HOUSES Inhabited	Uninhabited (U.), or Building (B.)	NAME and Surname of each Person	RELATION to Head of Family	CONDITION as to Marriage
					Jane Ritchin	daur	
					Hannah Jenkinson	Mother in law	W
117	Kirkland	5	1		William Stephenson	Head	
					Esther do	Wife	
					William H do	Son	
					Jacob J do	Son	
					John do	Son	
	do	6		U			
118	do	7	1		John Hunter	Head	
					Alice do	Wife	
					Patrick Hards	Boarder	
					Felix Givan	do	
					William Muir	do	
119	do	8	1		Henry Lobb	Head	
					Ann do	Wife	
					Anglan do	daur	
					William do	Son	
					Henry do	Son	
					Joseph do	Son	
					Charley do	Son	
					Ellen do	daur	
120	do No 9		1		Mary Jane Hoskin	Wife	
					Mary E. do	daur	
					Thomas H do	Son	
					Emily do	daur	

| | Total of Houses... | 4 | 4 | | Total of Males and Females | |

NOTE.—Draw the pen through such of the words of the headings as are inappropriate.

Table 3. An excerpt from the 1881 Census for part of Lamplugh Parish
by kind permission of Cumbria Record Office and Local Studies Library, Whitehaven

Town or Village or Hamlet of	Urban Sanitary District of	Rural Sanitary District of	Ecclesiastical Parish or District of
		Whitehaven	Lamplugh

last day Females	Rank, Profession, or OCCUPATION	WHERE BORN	(1) Deaf-and-Dumb (2) Blind (3) Imbecile or Idiot (4) Lunatic
4		Cumberland Lamplugh	
67		do Ennerdale	
	Iron Miner	Cornwall	
28	do Wife	Cumberland Whiteha	
	Scholar	do do	
		do do	
		do do	
	Iron Miner	do Branthwaite	
36	do Wife	do Keswick	
	do m	Ireland	
	do m	do	
	do m	Cumberland Dean	
	do m	Cornwall Roche	
46	do Wife	do Lanivet	
19	do daur	do do	
	do m	do do	
	do m	do do	
	Scholar	do do	
	do	do do	
5	do	do do	
26	Iron Miner Wife	do	
8	Scholar	Somerset Oldbow	
	do	do do	
2		Cumberland Lamplugh	
105			

Other activities including football, cricket, bowling and wrestling were popular. Many towns and villages had brass bands. As leisure time and incomes increased, cycling and hill walking became fashionable. Walking had always been a favourite pastime especially at weekends when families, perhaps after church, would take a stroll along local lanes and footpaths.

> *A typical example is that of a shot firer at the Florence mine who loved walking in the countryside. He had a set routine. Every day after his shift, he would wash and change and have a bite to eat. Then he would walk for about four or five miles before returning home for his main meal. At about eight o'clock he would stroll round to the nearby club and have one pint, after which he returned home and was always in bed by nine o'clock. A moderate man who worked in the mines for well over forty years. He was made redundant in the 1960s at the age of sixty four. It was around this time that he acquired a new grandchild and so he continued his daily walks, only this time pushing a pram! A favourite reply among miners when asked what sort of day it was on the surface was, "It's a babby day", meaning it was a good day for pram pushing!*

The Harps Club on Yeathouse Road, Frizington, had two doors, one at either end. As the miners came off first shift on a Friday afternoon, the landlord would have pints of beer lined up on the long bar, in readiness for them – but – they were limited to one pint each. Then they had to go home and hand over their wages to the wife before they were allowed to come back for more.

Not all miners frequented the public houses after work although it was understandable that the men needed to imbibe some form of liquid after a long strenuous shift underground in the dusty atmosphere. In one particular household the children would be asked to keep a look out for the miners coming home or listen for the sound of their clogs as they came down the street. As soon as their father appeared a large mug of tea was placed on a corner of the kitchen table, which the miner quickly swallowed before going into the scullery to wash and change his clothes.

The churches provided not only spiritual support, but also the opportunities for recreational activities with clubs and choirs. Working Men's Clubs and Reading Rooms were set up in the late 1800s with libraries providing the opportunity for further education. The YMCA encouraged Debating Societies and the Worker's Educational Association ran a variety of lectures and courses in the early 1900s.

Sadly, many of these interests had to be curtailed as the market for Cumbrian iron ore began to decline at the end of the 19th century. Families were forced to uproot once again and move to other areas to find work. Many men travelled to South Africa to work in the gold mines. Some would be waved off at the railway station never to be seen again but others returned home three or four years later with stories and, hopefully, some extra funds. As the growth of the nuclear industry increased in West Cumbria after the Second World War, many men left the mines to work at Sellafield and so a way of life, which had continued in the same families for many generations, changed forever.

Thankfully our children will never know the hardship their ancestors endured as they struggled to earn their living in the mines, but we must ensure that they are made fully aware of the story of the "Red Men".

Figure 50. Miners' houses, recently modernized, between Wath Brow and Cleator

Index

Bold type shows main references

Accidents, causes of, 9, 13, 27, 33, 34, 47, 49, 53, 54, 59, 71

Adits, see drifts

Agnes Mine, 32, 34, 37

Barite, 35

Beckermet & Beckermet Mines, 2, 15, **51-63**

Bessemer process, 10, 37

Bigrigg, 2, 9

Birks Mine, 9

Brockram, 4, 33, 53, 57

Calcite, 5

Carboniferous, 2, 5

Cleator, 13, 15, 16, 39, 47, 49

Cleator to Workington Railway, 10, 47

Cleator Moor & Cleator Moor Mines, 13, 15, 16, **37-49**, 51, 77

Clothing, Miners', 69

Coast to Coast Cycleway (C2C), 43, 47

Company system, 14, 65

Cornish immigrants, 27, 74-75

Crossfield Mine, 13, 38, 39, 43, 45, 49

Crossgill Mine, 13, 35, 37

Crowgarth Mine, 9, 16, 38, 39, 44, 49

Cumberland Iron Ore Miners and Kindred Trades Federation, 33, 68

Cumberland Miner, 33, 68, 72

Dolomite, 9

Drift, 6, 11, 16, 21, 47, 57

Egremont & Egremont Mines, 2, 5, 9, 15, 16, **51-63**

Emigration, 16, 49, 77

Faults, 2, 4, 5, 20, 39, 40, 41, 51, 53, 63

Flats, 5, 6, 31, 51, 53, 55, 63

Florence Mine, 5, 6, 15, 16, 17, **55-60**, 62

Frizington & Frizington Mines, 9, 15, 16, 17, **29-37**, 40, 51, 69, 72, 76

Gangue, 5, 6, 24

Gavan -Duffy. T, 15, 76

Gillfoot Park Mine, 52- 55

Great Depression of the 1930s, 15, 29, 37, 49, 51

Haile Moor Mine, 16, **56-59**, 63, 67-69

Hematite, 2-6, 20, 40, 44, 49, 53, 54, 56, 63

High House & High House Mine, **29-37**

Immigration, 27, 66, 69, 74

Irish immigrants, 27, 74-75

Jacktrees Mine, 9, 13

Kelton Mine, 2, 4, 5, 16, **20-27**
Kidney ore, 5, 35, 44
Kirkland Village, 15, 20, 25, 27, 40, 69, 74-75
Knockmurton Mine, 2, 20-27, 69

Lamplugh & Lamplugh Mines, 2, 10, 16,
20-27, 74-75
Leases and conditions of, 40, 45-6
Levels, 11, 12
Limestone, 2, 4, 20, 31, 32, 40, 41, 45, 51, 53,
55, 57
Lindow, Jonas, 45-46
Living conditions, 66, 71, 73-76
Longlands Mine, 45-46
Lonsdale Mine (Frizington), 29, 30, 32, 37
Lord Leconfield & Leconfield Mine (see
Crowgarth Mine)

Mining related accidents, deaths, injuries
and disease, see Accidents and causes of
Margaret Mine, **29-37**, 71
Moor Row, 9, 39, 40
Montreal Mine, 13, **38-47**
Mowbray Mine, 30, 35, 37

Outputs, 2, 9-10, 15-16, 24, 25, 31-33, 40, 44,
45, 51, 54, 57, 61

Parkside & Parkside Mine, 13, 14, **29-37**
Permian rocks, 4, 5, 33
Phosphorus impurity, 10, 31, 33
Population totals, 15, 16, 27, 29, 37, 49, 51

Quartz (Silica), 5, 10

River Ehen, 45, 52-54
River Keekle, 39, 40, 43, 49
Robberies, 12, 33, 49
Rowrah and Kelton Fell Railway, 21, 22, 25

Specularite, 5, 35
Skiddaw Group rocks, 4, 20
St Bees Sandstone, 2, 4, 15, 33
Stirling family & Stirling's Hospital, 43, 47
Strikes, 14, 37, 51, 53
Subsidences, 16, 31, 32, 35, 39, 44, 46, 49,
53, 54
Townhead & Clints Mines, 52, 54

Ullcoats Mine, 15, 57, 63

Vein, 4, 5, 20, 51, 53, 55
Vug, 5, 6, 57

Whinnah Pit, 10
William Baird & Co, 24
Whitehaven, Cleator and Egremont
Railway, 10, 20, 24, 31, 33, 47, 49
Whitehaven News, 34, 47
Working conditions, 67-72
Wyndham Mine, 52-54

Yeathouse & Yeathouse Mine, 10, 32, 35

List of Figures

Chapter 1 Location of the Hematite Mines

Figure 1.   Map of the West Cumbria Iron Ore Mining Area.
Figure 2.   Diagram showing how hematite occurs.
Figure 3.   Vug in roof of a gallery in Florence Mine, Egremont.
Figure 4.   Photograph of a Spar Box.
Figure 5.   Display in the Chicago Field Museum of Natural History.

Chapter 2 The Rise and Fall of Iron Ore Mining

Figure 6.   Whinnah Pit at Lamplugh about 1900.
Figure 7.   Diagram showing the typical layout of a mine.
Figure 8.   A labourer emptying a 'modern' ore chute before 1980.
Figure 9.   The metal box still carrying the Lingla Beck at Parkside near Cleator Moor.
Figure 10. Florence Mine just before closure in 2008.

Chapter 3 Lamplugh and Kirkland

Figure 11. The Lamplugh Mine area.
Figure 12. Map of the Kelton and Knockmurton Mines.
Figure 13. Knockmurton Fell and the Rowrah and Kelton Fell Railway.
Figure 14. A contemporary watercolour of Knockmurton Mine about 1919.
Figure 15. The teapot presented to William Ramsay.
Figure 16. A collapse above a hematite vein at Kelton Mine.

Chapter 4 Frizington

Figure 17. A shift at Lonsdale Mine, Frizington about 1900.
Figure 18. Map of the Mines near Parkside.
Figure 19. "The Boilers".
Figure 20. The Margaret Mine, Frizington after the fire 1911.
Figure 21. A barrel roofed dynamite hut.
Figure 22. A Time Line for Frizington Mines.

Chapter 5 Around Cleator Moor

Figure 23.   The Cleator Moor Iron Mines.
Figure 24.   The Mural in Cleator Moor Square.
Figure 25.   Diagram to show how both coal and iron were mined from Montreal Pit No. 4.
Figure 26.   Sandstone block inscribed with a verse from "Cleator Moor"
             by Norman Nicholson.
Figure 27.   The abandoned rock crusher in 2009 on the site of Montreal Pit No. 4.
Figure 28.   The Black Ship.
Figure 29.   A 1917 postcard of Lord Leconfield's Pit, Cleator Moor.
Figure 30.   The Longlands Mine in 1916.
Figure 31.   Longlands Pit No.1 in 2009.
Figure 32.   A way-marker on the Coast to Coast Cycleway.

Chapter 6 Egremont and Beyond

Figure 33.   Map of the Egremont Mining Area.
Figure 34.   A cross-section to show how hematite occurs under Egremont.
Figure 35.   The collapse of Gillfoot Pit No. 6, June 2005.
Figure 36.   The Ehen Mine collapse near Egremont.
Figure 37.   The deep mines south of Egremont.
Figure 38.   A drift at Florence mine in the 1990s.
Figure 39.   The aerial ropeway near Haile Moor Mine.
Figure 40.   The electric winding engine at Haile Moor Mine in 1950s.
Figure 41.   Roof reinforcements at Haile Moor Mine.
Figure 42.   Bill Kilgour and Ike Wilson drilling a new heading after 1945.
Figure 43.   Bogies used underground at Florence Mine.
Figure 44.   Ken Drinkwater operating a motorized shovel to load ore.
Figure 45.   Loading ore at Beckermet Pit No. 1.
Figure 46.   The winding wheel at Florence Mine.

Chapter 7 The "Red Men" and their memories

Figure 47.   Roof conditions at Haile Moor Mine in the 1950s.
Figure 48.   Alf Verroa firing a shot at Haile Moor Mine in the 1950s.
Figure 49.   Angelo da Crema and Carlo Lamberi drilling in wet conditions.
Figure 50.   Miners' houses, recently modernized, between Wath Brow and Cleator.